Truckstop Honeymoon's Guide to Touring for Young Musicians

Featuring

Sadie

Vega

Julian

Esther

by Mike West

1. Getting Ready for Tour

When you go on tour, you have to bring a lot of stuff.

your clothes

suitcase

some light reading

a camera

water-proof boots

crayons

your elephant with big red pants

pull-up diapers

a backpack

HUGGIES

toothbrush

200 piece lego set of a rocket

toothpaste

hairbrush

And don't forget your Instruments.

guitar

ukulele

fiddle

and accordion

...maybe not the accordion

There are some things you don't need to bring on tour.

your dog

the chickens

your collection of
interesting rocks

and your really cool,
really heavy,
old-fashioned typewriter

When everything is packed, it's time to load the van...

...carefully!

2. Driving

On tour you drive a lot.

While you drive, you can take in the scenery.

You can draw pictures of your family.

WE WILL, WE WILL ROCK YOU!

You can sing Queen songs really loudly.

You can even have a picnic in the van

with real cheese flavored popcorn,

pistachios,

satsumas,

and boiled peanuts.

Then pretty soon it's time to...

...clean out the van.

3. Flying

Sometimes on tour you fly.

Sometimes you don't.

When you do fly, there is lots to do.

You can watch movies and cartoons all night long on a tiny little TV in the back of someone else's seat.

You can eat really hot spaghetti out of an aluminum foil tray on a very cool folding table.

And you can play with all the buttons and switches in the armrest of your seat...

...until the flight attendant comes.

You should try to get some sleep on the plane.

That way you will feel better when you land.

If you fly to a foreign country,
you will have to go through **Immigrations**.

This is where an immigration officer makes sure you look
just like the photo in your passport.

Then you collect your luggage from the carousel

and drive some more.

4. Accommodation

The first place you go to is your **accommodation**.
Your accommodation is where you sleep when you are on tour.

Sometimes you get a bed.

Sometimes you get a couch.

Sometimes you get the floor.

Sometimes you get a couch and the floor.

Sometimes you stay in a motel.

air conditioning

T.V.

a queen size bed that fits
four if you sleep crosswise

electric kettle

instant hot
chocolate

Sometimes you stay in a tent.

rain

leaky tent fly

lucky you
brought
those boots

sticky mud

But mostly, you stay with nice people like...

...Kevin and Jean. Kevin and Jean live in Dorset, England.

They have a dog named Abbie, a dog named Hattie Brown and a rooster named Clegg. Kevin and Hattie Brown have bad legs. But watch out for Clegg. Clegg does not have bad legs. Clegg can jump very high.

He has
sharp spurs!

And this is Dougie and Gleny.

Dougie and Gleny live in Newcastle, Australia. Dougie plays bass and can fix almost anything. Gleny plays fiddle and knows lots of songs that little kids shouldn't sing.

Dougie can show you how to make a "Roach Disco" from an empty match box and some sticky tape. If you don't know what a "Roach Disco" is, see the next page.

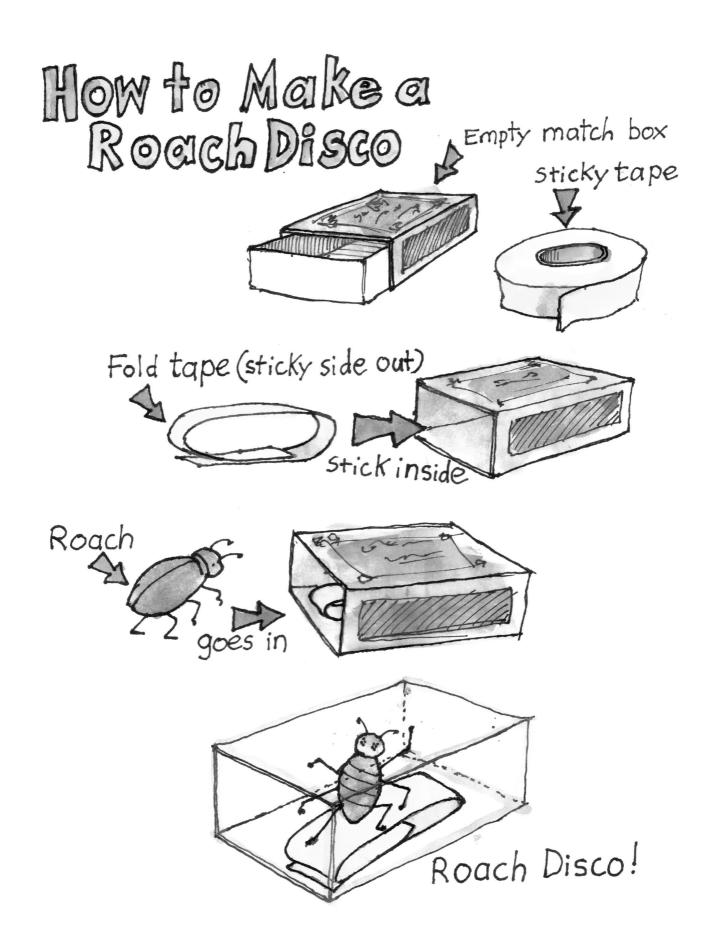

How to Make a Roach Disco

Empty match box

sticky tape

Fold tape (sticky side out)

Stick inside

Roach

goes in

Roach Disco!

Accommodation can be fun and educational.

5. The Gig

After you check into your accommodation, you go to **the venue**.
The venue is the place you will play.

It might look
like this...

...or it might look like this.

The first thing you do at the venue is **soundcheck**.
Soundcheck is when you make sure all the sound equipment is working properly.

Check your microphones. To check a microphone, you must count to two over and over again. I don't know why, that's just how it's done.

Check your amplifier. Is it making any strange noises?

And remember, it is very important not to tangle your cables!

Then you go to the **green room** to relax before the show.

Green rooms are usually black. They usually have food and refreshments there...

...except when they don't.

Finally, it's *showtime!*

When you play, the audience claps and claps...

...or yaps and yaps.

Either way, you play the best you can.

And when it's all over, you get to go back to your accommodation.

6. Busking

Sometimes you go **busking** on tour. This is when you play on the street and people throw money into your instrument case.

Or they tell you to go and play somewhere else.

Sometimes people give you food when you busk.

At the farmers' market, a farmer might give you tomatoes.

At the Oregon Country Fair, a stilt walker might give you banana bread.

But usually people just throw coins.

With the money you make from busking, you can buy souvenirs. You find all sorts of treasures on tour.

more books

model plane

used clothes

plastic troll with some of its hair missing

Can you find any of these?

Alligator, trike, bone handled butter knife, sewing machine, globe, teddy bear, cracked teapot, plastic horse, blue truck, feathered hat.

7. Going Home

Touring is fun. You go exciting places.

You eat exotic food.

blackcurrent
cordial

beans on toast

But sooner or later it is time to go home,

back to all the things you miss.

The End